Curious George and the Great Shape Hunt

Written by Jessica Wollman

Houghton Mifflin Harcourt
Boston   New York

Curious George wants to find shapes!
Can you help George?

Look at the bike, George!
You will find two circles.
Can you see two circles?

George wants to discover
more shapes.
Can you help George find a
new shape?

Look at the basket, George!
You will find a new shape!
The basket is a rectangle.

What shape will George
find next?
Can you help him find a
new shape?

Look at the sandwich, George!
The man's sandwich is a square!

The man cut the sandwich in half.
His square sandwich is now two triangles.

Shapes can be very yummy!